Piano Magic Pieces
Book 2

by Jane Sebba

with consultants Sheena Roberts, Ruth Stone and David Wright

Illustrated by Alison Dexter

133 St. Pancras Way,
London NW1 9NB

Tel: 020-7482-5424
Fax: 020-7482-5424
E-mail: dot@dotsonline.co.uk
Web: www.dotsonline.co.uk

A & C Black · London

I've got sixpence

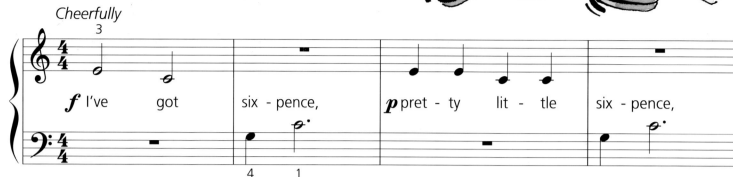

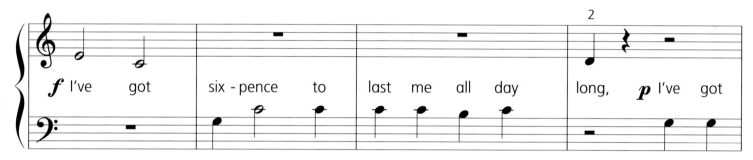

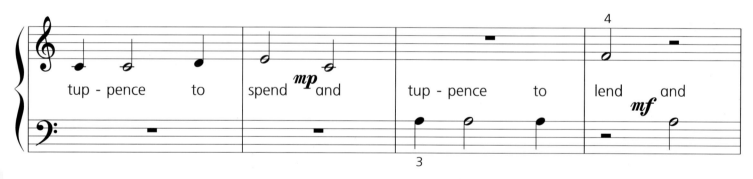

2

Violin melody by Beethoven

Brightly

mf

mp

p

Caged bear

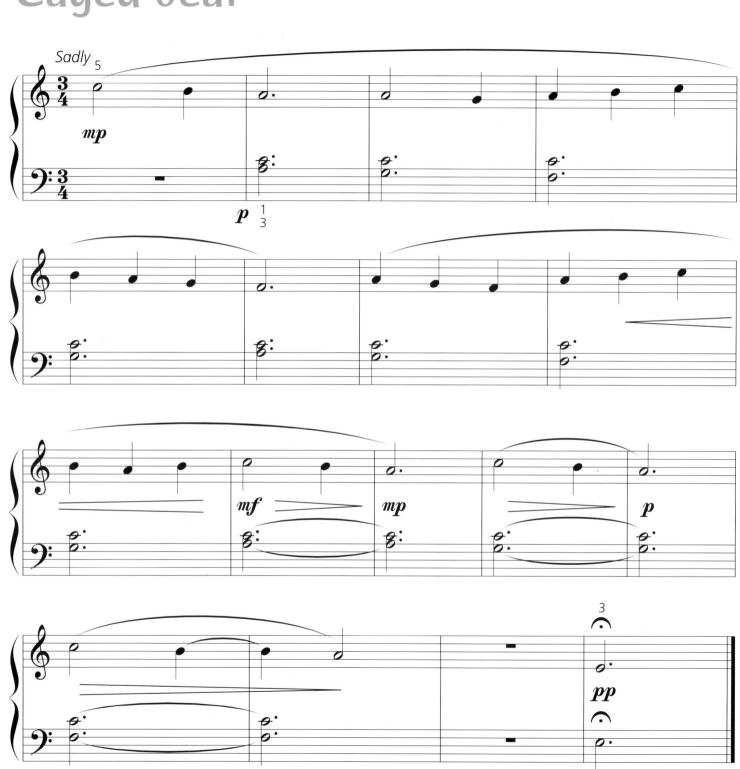

A laugh a second

Play the music as written, then play it again. Change the RH chords like this. Play three black keys together, or two black keys together, where you see these signs:

Play them at any octave.

A little waltz

In a singing style

5

Ruth's busy day

Tapping keys

1° play as written   2° play RH one octave higher, LH one octave lower

Ruth's fanfare

Winter

Slow and desolate

Winter improvisation

At the end of *Winter*, make up some wintry music. Follow these rules:

1. You must play two notes at a time in each hand – whether your hands play together or one after the other.

2. Each set of two notes you play must be a fifth apart.

3. The fifths may be anywhere on the keyboard – high, low or in the middle.

4. You must end on this fifth:

At the end of your winter improvisation, play *Spring.* (What do you notice about the beginning of *Spring*?)

Spring improvisations

Where you see these pictures, make up some music to describe them during the pauses.

Use RH to make the music of birds singing.

Use LH for the music of buds opening.

Use both hands for squiggling tadpoles.

ped. (optional)

Spring

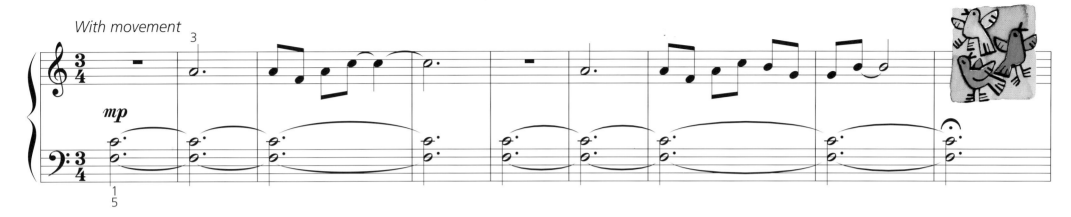

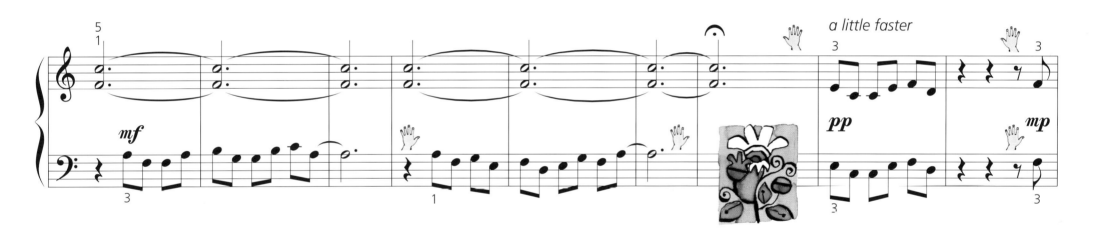

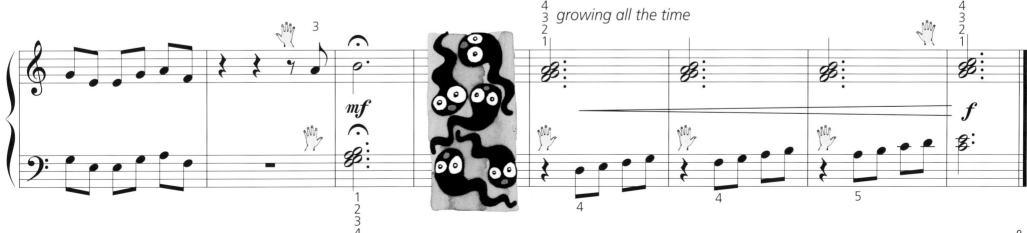

9

Ducklings test the pond

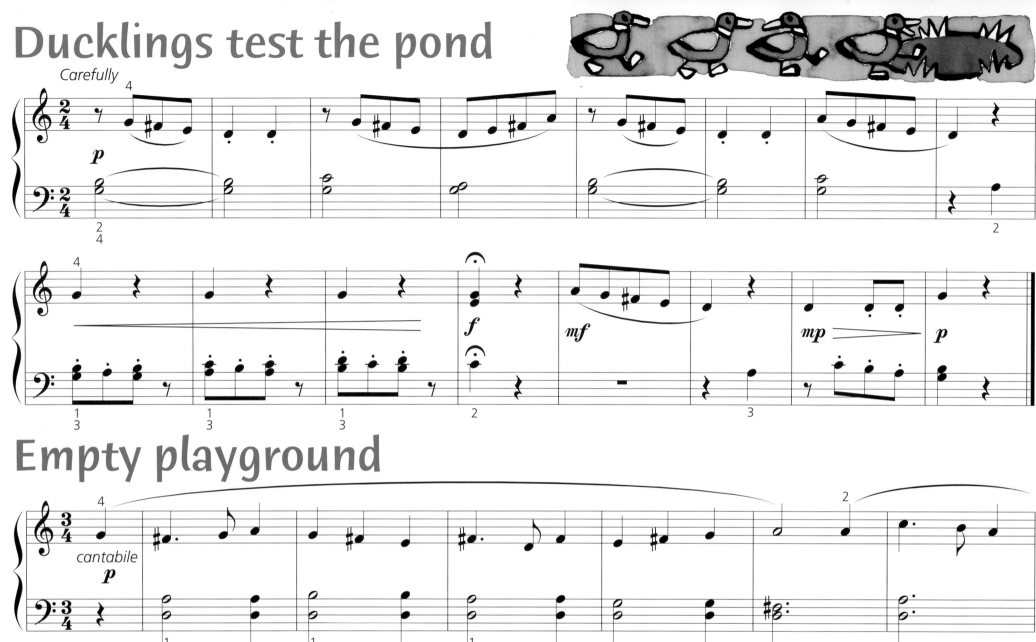

Empty playground

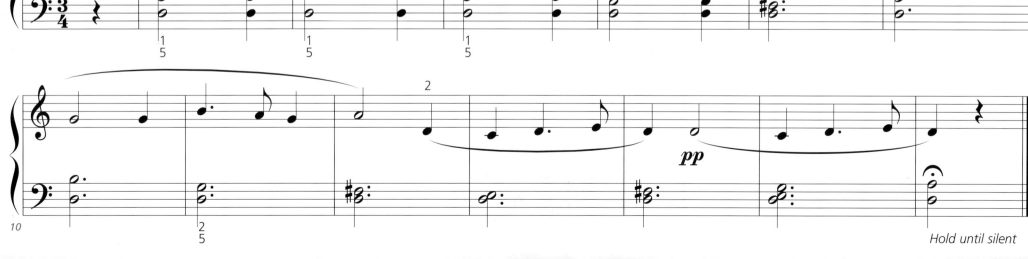

Hold until silent

Ants build a nest

Pianissimo, staccatissimo and fast

Clockwork mice

A cheeky tune

Two-handed chase

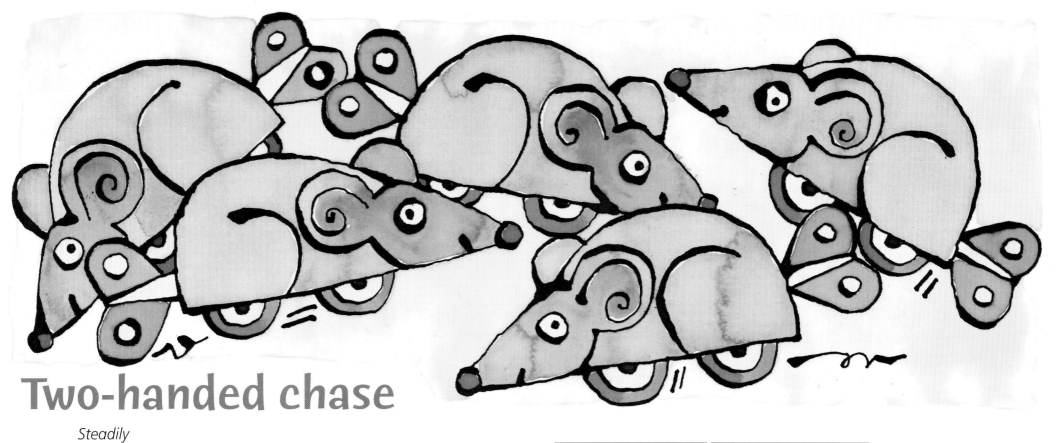

Dreamtime

Little brown jug

Spook on the staircase

Ghost in the garden

Follow the leader

Playfully

Animal fair

Steadily plodding along

mf

f I went to the a-ni-mal fair, the birds and the beasts were

there. The big ba-boon by the light of the moon was comb-ing his au-burn hair. The

tempo ad lib.   *a tempo*   *tempo ad lib.*   *a tempo*

mon-key fell out of his bunk, bump! Slid down the e-le-phant's trunk, whee! ____ The e-le-phant sneezed and

fell on his knees, and what be-came of the mon-key, mon-key, mon-key, mon-key, mon-key, mon-key, monk?

Jane's zebras

Proudly cantering along

Just a simple melody

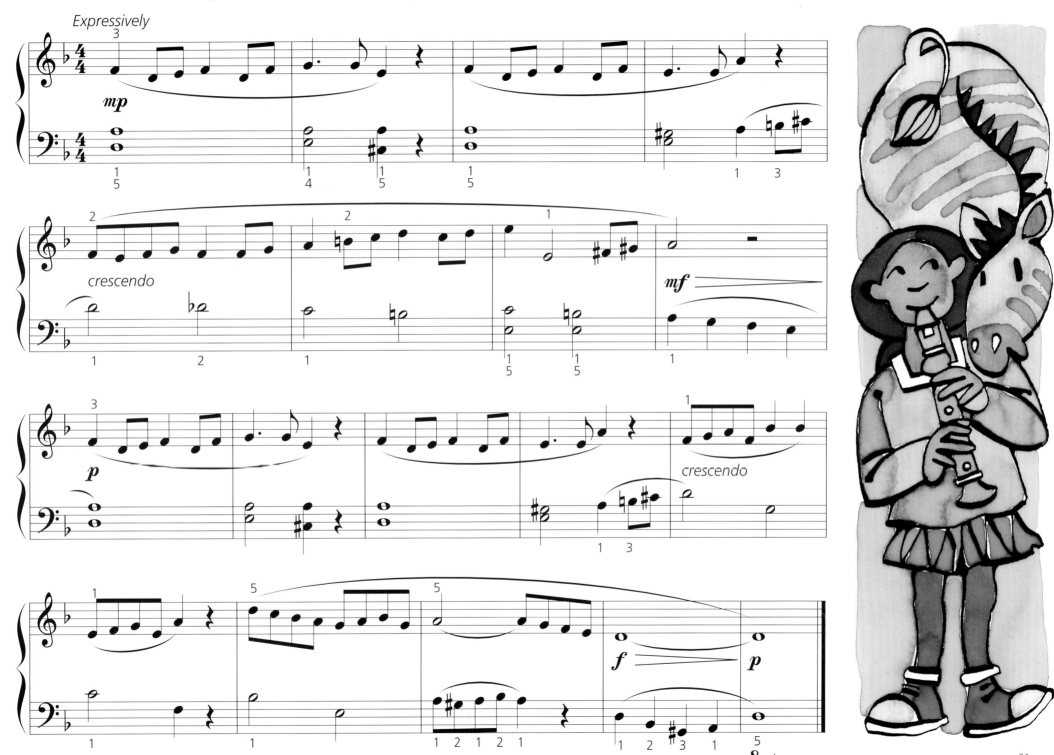

Variations on Twinkle, twinkle little star

Variation 1

Variation 2

A little slower

Variation 3

Even slower

legato

To your teacher

Piano Magic Pieces Books 1 and *2* have been devised as supplementary repertoire for their parent tutor, *Piano Magic*. They follow closely the technical and theoretical path of the tutor books. This close linkage with the tutors makes them especially useful to the beginner working through *Piano Magic*, but their carefully graded content makes them equally suitable for any beginner needing supplementary repertoire.

Piano Magic Tutor offers a fully integrated approach to musicianship through the progressive development of theory, technique, note reading, aural awareness, sightreading, improvising, transposing and composing. *Piano Magic Pieces* focuses on straightforward solo repertoire, but opportunities for improvising and composing are given, and of course opportunities for sightreading and transposing can be made at any point.

New notes are introduced in the same order as in the tutors except where musical effect won over adherence to strict order. Your attention is drawn to these exceptions by the little crocodile symbol in the music.

Where Piano Magic Pieces Book 2 begins
Piano Magic Tutor Book 1 teaches the beginner the written notes from Middle C down to F in the left hand and up to G in the right, plus the two Cs an octave above and below. This is where *Piano Magic Pieces Book 2* begins. By the end of the book, your pupil will be using the written notes from the second G below Middle C up to the second F above, along with their accidentals.

Solo repertoire develops the beginner pianist's independence, but there will be many details with which your pupil will need your help. The following notes on some of the pieces refer to the place of each in the general progression and its specific focus. In addition, symbols within the music draw your pupil's attention to details with which your help may be required.

 This little crocodile draws attention to details which may need some extra explanation from you.

 This little hand warns the player of an imminent hand position change. (They are not given after page 9.)

Note range:

Page 2 *I've got sixpence*: focuses on revising known notes in a simple melody which needs to flow evenly between left and right hand.

Page 3 *Violin melody by Beethoven*: further revision of known notes in a melody which demands close attention to articulation.

New notes:

Page 4 *Caged bear*: focuses on left hand chordal accompaniment to a sustained right hand melody (the inverse of *Caged bird* in *Piano Magic Tutor*).

Page 5 *A laugh a second*: you may like to teach this by rote since it contains an unfamiliar accidental in one part, and an optional improvisation in the other. Take turns with your pupil to play the left hand or right hand part, and aim for comedy!

Page 5 *A little waltz*: the little hand symbols in the music warn the player of the approaching hand position changes, which provide technical progression in this piece.

Page 6 *Ruth's busy day*: quavers (eighth notes) appear for the first time, set within a strongly rhythmic but supportive left hand accompaniment. After the first position change, the right hand moves down through a sequence of changes which might be extended on down the keyboard as a separate technical exercise.

Page 6 *Tapping keys*: the fun of this piece lies in the interlocking left hand and right hand quavers (eighth notes) – the thumbs take it in turns to lead, and in the suggestion to move both hands out an octave in each direction.

Page 7 *Ruth's fanfare*: this exciting fanfare gives opportunities for reading and playing octaves with hands together in similar motion, as well as working within a new level of rhythmic diversity.

Page 8 *Winter*: the dotted crotchet (quarter note) appears for the first time. The piece is technically more advanced, and rhythmically more complex than anything met so far. But the pace is slow, allowing

plenty time for assimilation. *Winter* leads from its improvisation of bare fifths straight into the next piece, *Spring*, and may form a sequence with it.

Page 9 *Spring*: the tempo is intended to be more free and dynamic than the icy exactness required in *Winter*. Perhaps the notes of *Spring* might be taught by rote, given its free rhythmic character and the opportunities to insert three little windows of improvisation. The whole sequence might then be memorised for a special performance.

New notes:

Page 10 *Ducklings test the pond*: focuses on neat finger work and clear articulation with a lot of practice in playing F sharp in the right hand.

Page 10 *Empty playground*: note the stretch of a sixth in the left hand.

Page 11 *Ants build a nest*: more practice with F sharp, neat finger work and faster hand position changes within a seven beat metre. Your pupil might enjoy the alternative harmonic effect of playing F natural in bars 9, 11 and 13.

New notes:

Page 12 *Clockwork mice*: first and second time bars.

Page 12 *A cheeky tune*: key signature.

Page 13 *Two-handed chase*: first and second time bars again; key signature.

Page 14 *Dreamtime*: focuses on the slur, both on and off the beat.

New notes:

Page 15 *Little brown jug*: new notes and a new key signature.

Page 16 *Spook on the staircase*: this and the

following piece may be played one after the other. The *sforzando* may need explanation.

Page 17 *Ghost in the garden*: the illustrations tell the story. The left hand is the ghost, light, airy and nebulous. The right hand is the jaunty, unsuspecting walker.

New notes:

Page 18 *Follow the leader*: compound time.

Page 19 *Animal fair*: the whole tone run in the third system uses exactly the same notes as that in *Hickory Dickory Rock*, *Piano Magic Tutor Book 2*.

Page 20 *Jane's zebras*: chromatic fingerings and notation.

Page 21 *Just a simple melody*: focuses on more advanced independent hand movement, and the third finger pivoting over the thumb.

Page 22–23 *Variations on Twinkle, twinkle little star*: your pupil may enjoy the challenge of preparing a performance of these variations.

Acknowledgements

The author and publishers would like to give special thanks to the following people who have generously given their assistance:

Rosanna Bortoli, Alison Dexter, Dorothy Moir, Stuart Murray, Cath Rasbash, Simon Ray-Hills, Sheena Roberts, Ana Sanderson, Sarah Stirling, Ruth Stone, David Wright.

All original music and arrangements are by Jane Sebba, except for A cheeky tune *by David Wright,* © *David Wright 1999.*

First published 1999
by A & C Black (Publishers) Ltd
35 Bedford Row, London WC1R 4JH
© *1999 Jane Sebba*
Illustrations © *Alison Dexter*
Edited by Sheena Roberts
Music setting by Jenny Fisher
Printed in China through Colorcraft Ltd

ISBN 0-7136-5211-X